Essential
Music Theory

San Marco
Publications

Mark Sarnecki

ISNB: 9781896499253

CONTENTS

1

When we write a story we use letters to make words. When we write a song we use notes to indicate sound. There are different types of notes. Some notes are hollow. Some notes are filled in. Some notes have lines attached to them. A note consists of a round part called the *note head*. A line attached to a note is called a *stem*.

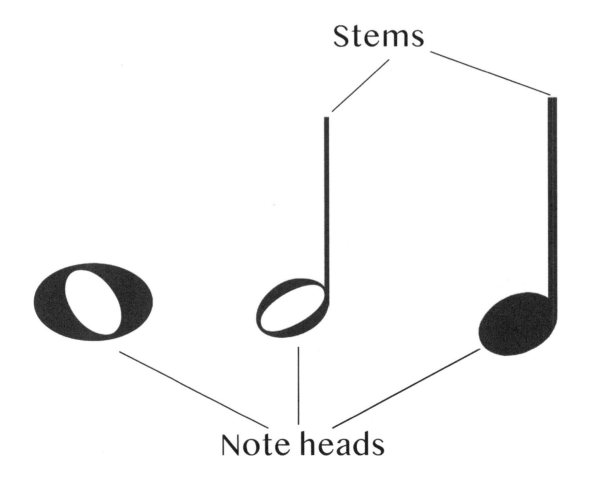

The Whole Note

The whole note is a hollow note without a stem. It receives 4 counts or beats.

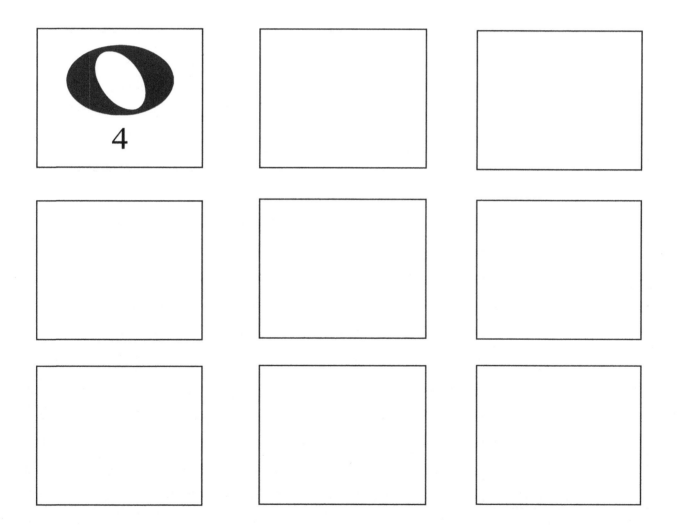

= 4 counts

1. Draw a whole note in each box. Write the number of counts the whole note receives under each note.

The Half Note

The half note is a hollow note with a stem. It receives 2 counts or beats.

= 2 counts

2. Draw a half note in each box. Write the number of counts the half note receives next to each note.

The Quarter Note

The quarter note is a solid note with a stem. It receives 1 count or beat.

= 1 count

3. Draw a quarter note in each box. Write the number of counts the quarter note receives next to each note.

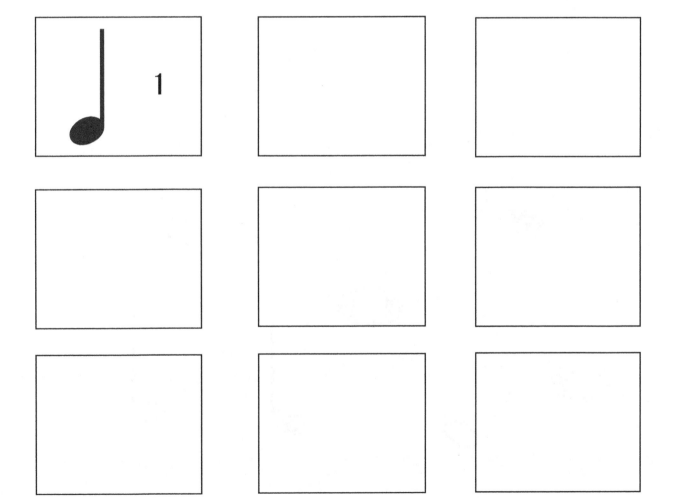

4. Draw:

A **circle**◯ around each whole note.
A **square**☐ around each half note.
A **triangle**△ around each quarter note.

5

1 whole note

equals

2 half notes

equals

4 quarter notes

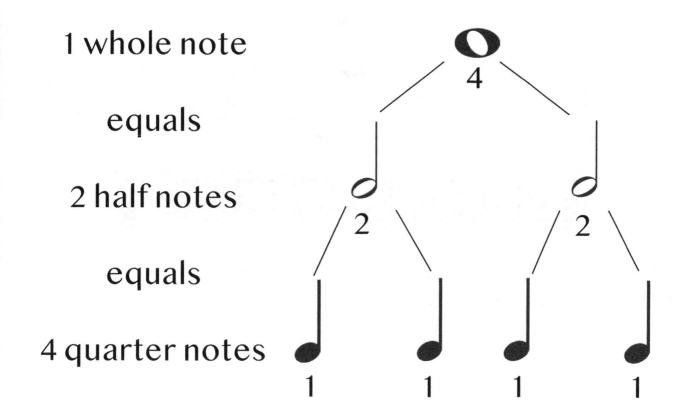

5. Write the name of the following notes and the number of counts.

_____ = _____ counts.

_____ = _____ counts.

_____ = _____ counts.

2

Lines and Spaces

Music is written on a *staff*. The staff consists of five lines. These five lines have four spaces between them. The lines and spaces are always numbered from the bottom up. The bottom line is Line 1, and the top line is Line 5. The bottom space is Space 1, and the top space is Space 4.

Line 5

Line 4

Line 3

Line 2

Line 1

Space 4

Space 3

Space 2

Space 1

1. Trace the following line notes. Then write them on the staves below.

2. Trace the following space notes. Then write them on the staves below.

3. Write the line number for each note.

2 ___ ___ ___ ___ ___

4. Write the space number for each note.

___ ___ ___ ___ ___ ___

5. Write line notes according to the numbers.

5   3   1   2   4   5

6. Write space notes according to the numbers.

4   2   1   3   4   1

Stem Direction

Many notes have stems. Stems may go up or stems may go down. There are specific rules for the direction of stems.

Stems Up

If a note is **below** the middle line its stem goes **up** and is placed on the **right**.

Stems Down

If a note is **above** the middle line its stem goes **down** and is placed on the **left**.

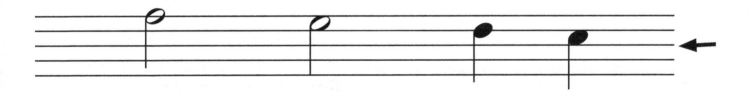

Stems Up or Down

If a note is **on** the middle line its stem may go **up** or **down**.

7. Write the line or space number for each note. Add a stem to each note.

3

THE KEYBOARD

The black keys are arranged in groups of
two   and   three.

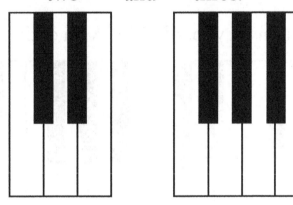

1. Circle all the groups of two black keys

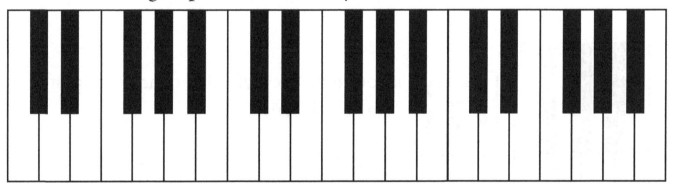

2. Circle all the groups of three black keys

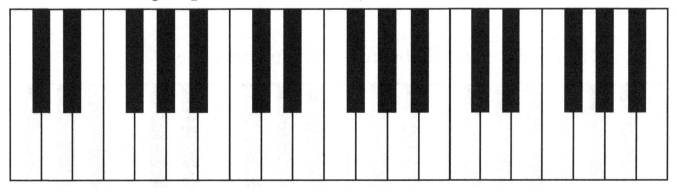

The Musical Alphabet consists of seven letters:

A B C D E F G

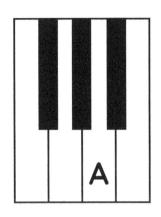 is found between the second and third keys of any group of three black keys.

3. Find all the **A**s on this keyboard. Print **A** on each one.

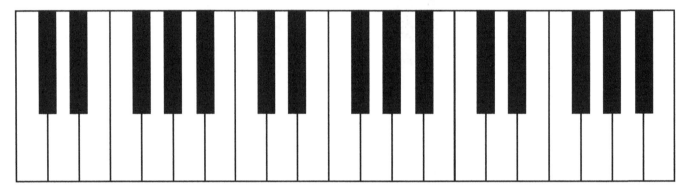

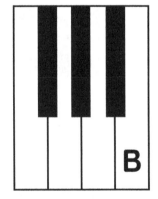 is found on the right side of any group of three black keys.

3. Find all the **B**s on this keyboard. Print **B** on each one.

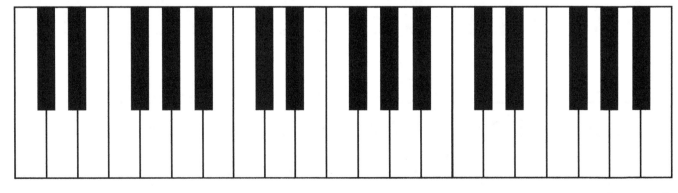

  **C** is found on the left side of any group of two black keys.

5. Find all the **C**s on this keyboard. Print **C** on each one.

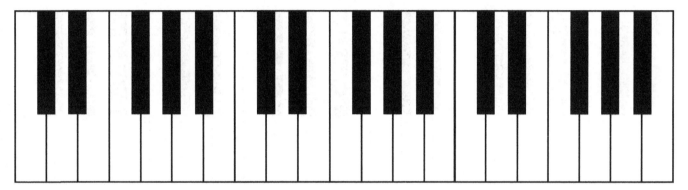

  **D** is found in the middle of any group of two black keys.

6. Find all the **D**s on this keyboard. Print **D** on each one.

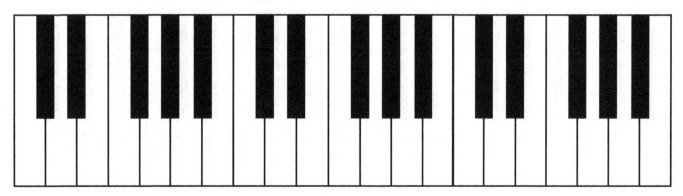

  is found on the right side of any group of two black keys.

7. Find all the **E**s on this keyboard. Print **E** on each one.

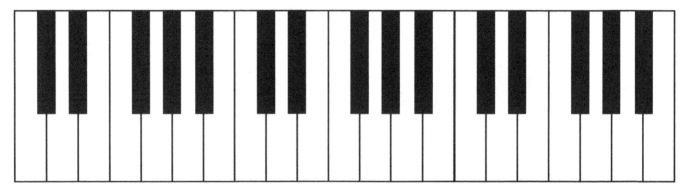

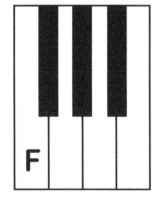 is found on the left side of any group of three black keys.

8. Find all the **F**s on this keyboard. Print **F** on each one.

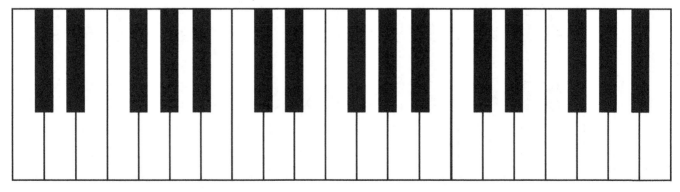

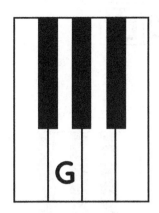 is found between the first and second keys of any group of three black keys.

9. Find all the **G**s on this keyboard. Print **G** on each one.

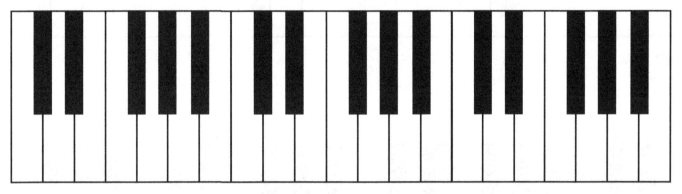

10. On the keyboard below, print the names of all the keys.

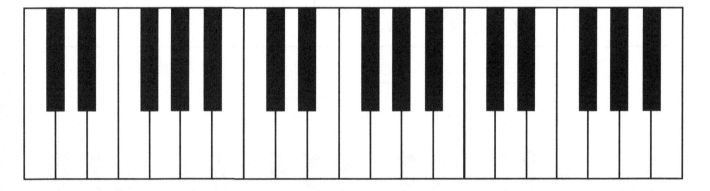

Good work!
You know the keyboard!

SPELLING FUN

1. Name the keys marked with stars to find words.

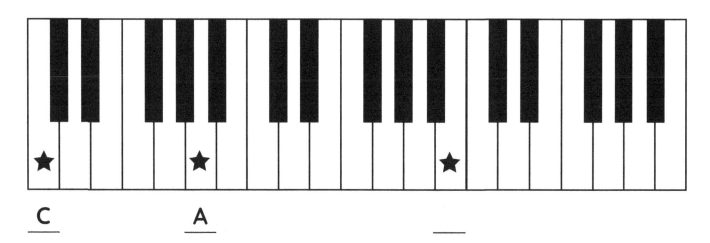

__C__   __A__   __

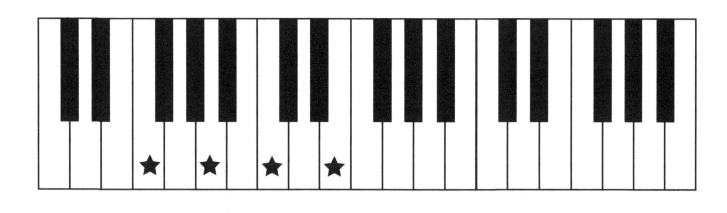

__ __ __ __

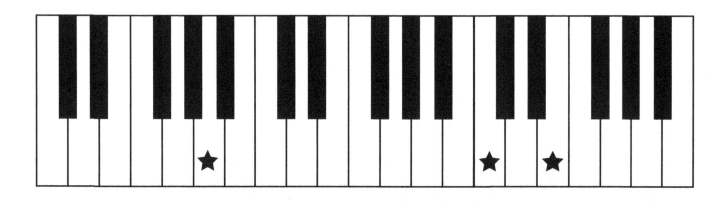

__   __ __

2. Write the following words on the keyboards below.

CAGE

EDGE

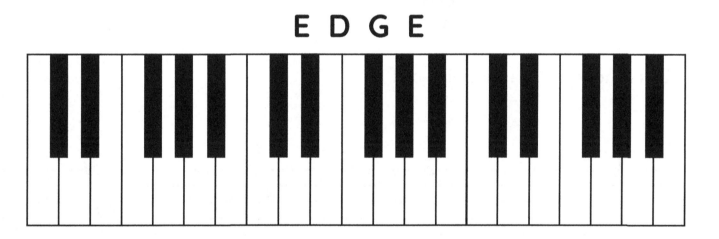

EGG

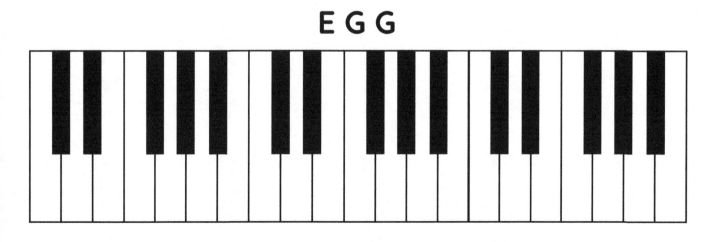

THE TREBLE CLEF

A *clef* is a sign placed at the beginning of the staff to tell us which note goes on each line and in each space. The word clef comes from a French word that means key. The most common clef is the *treble clef*. The higher notes are written in the treble clef. Some of the instruments that use the treble clef are the flute, clarinet, violin, trumpet, french horn, saxophone and piano.

This is a treble clef.

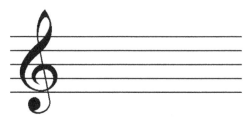

This is how you draw a treble clef.

1. Trace these treble clefs.

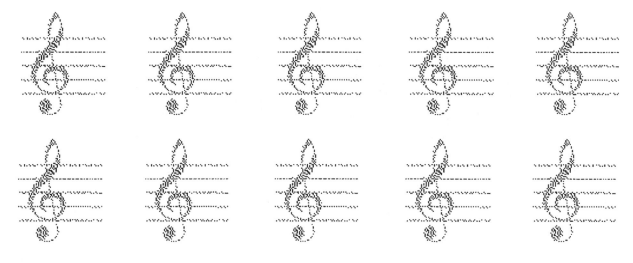

2. Draw treble clefs in the spaces below.

Notes on the Treble Staff

The first 3 notes we will learn on the treble staff are Middle C, D, and E. Middle C sits just under the staff and has a short line called a *ledger line* going through it.

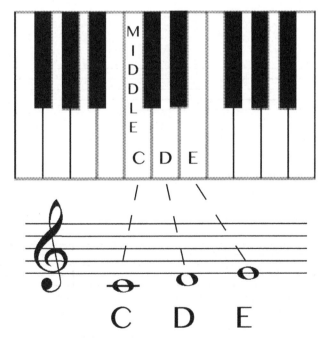

1. Draw a treble clef and the notes middle C, D and E. Draw lines to the corresponding keys on the keyboard.

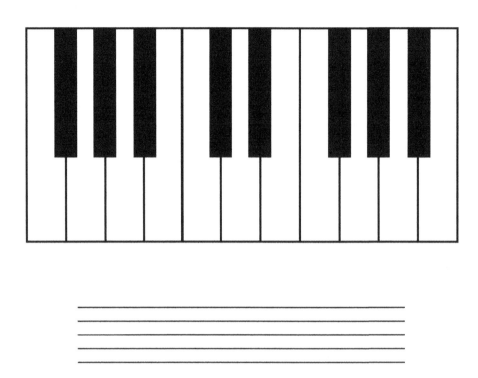

2. Write the following notes.

Middle C in half notes

D in quarter notes

E in whole notes

Middle C in whole notes

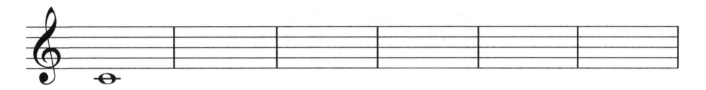

E in half notes

D in whole notes

Middle C in quarter notes

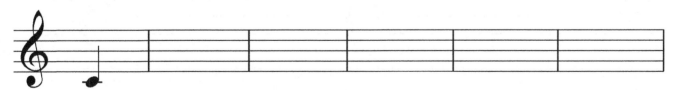

4

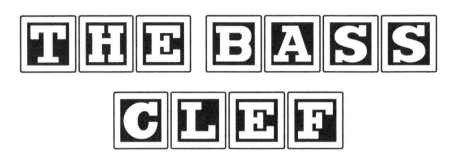

The second most common clef is the *bass clef*. The bass clef is used for instruments with a low sound. Some of these instruments are: the double bass, cello, tuba, trombone, and piano. Because they have such a large range, instruments like the piano and organ use both the treble and bass clefs.

This is a bass clef:

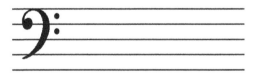

This is how you draw a bass clef.

1.   2.   3.

1. Trace these bass clefs.

2. Draw bass clefs in the spaces below.

Notes on the Bass Staff

The first 3 notes we will learn on the bass staff are A, B, and Middle C. Middle C sits just above the staff and has a ledger line going through it.

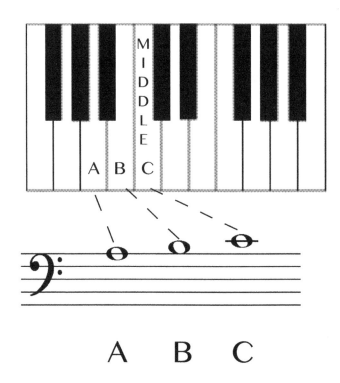

A   B   C

1. Write the following notes.

Middle C in quarter notes

B in whole notes

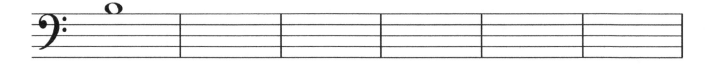

Middle C in half notes

A in quarter notes

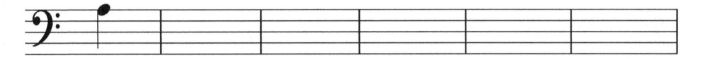

B in whole notes

A in half notes

B in quarter notes

 Lesson 4

2. Name the notes and write the number of counts under each one.

Name: ____ ____ ____ ____ ____

Count: ____ ____ ____ ____ ____

Name: ____ ____ ____ ____ ____

Count: ____ ____ ____ ____ ____

Name: —— ____ ____ ____ ____

Count: ____ ____ ____ ____ ____

Name: ____ ____ ____ ____ ____

Count: ____ ____ ____ ____ ____

Lesson 4

Music Match

Draw line to match the notes with the correct answers.

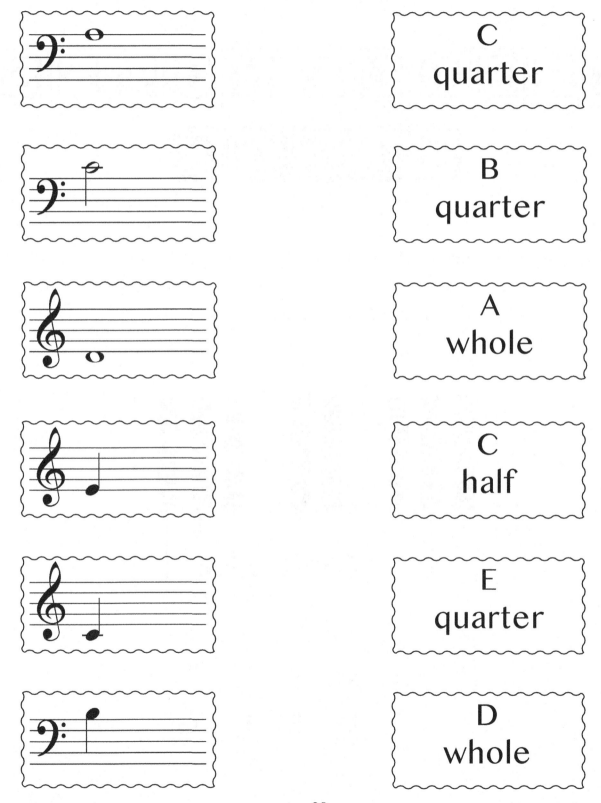

5

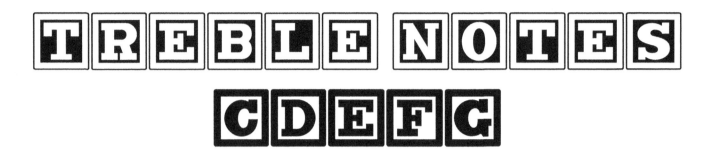

Here are the notes C-D-E-F-G on the treble staff. There are two new notes: F and G. F is in the first space and G is on the second line. On the keyboard they occur in alphabetical order after C-D-E.

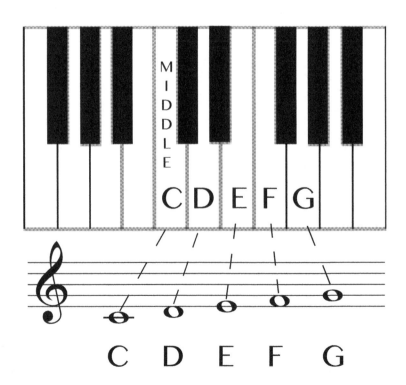

C   D   E   F   G

1. Name the following notes.

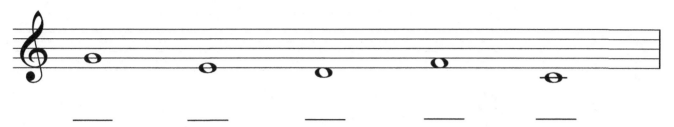

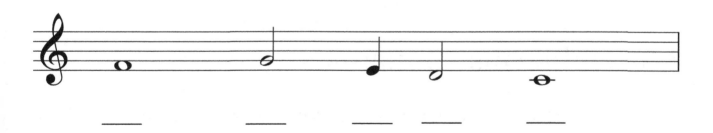

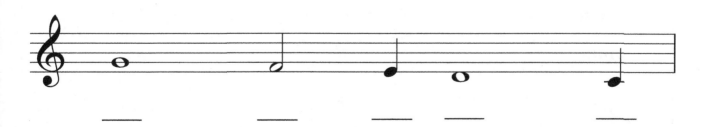

2. Write the following notes. Use quarter notes.

D   G   E   F   C   F

3. Write the following notes. Use half notes.

F   D   C   E   G   D

4. Write the following notes. Use whole notes.

C   D   E   F   G   C

Musical Terms - Dynamics

Music may be loud or soft. Words or signs are written on the music to tell us how loud or soft to play. These are called *dynamics*. Here are two of the most important ones.

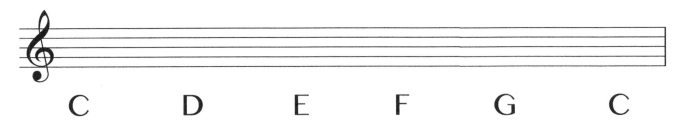

Term	Abbreviation	Meaning
piano	*p*	soft
forte	*f*	loud

6

Here are the notes F-G-A-B-C on the bass staff. There are two new notes: F and G. F is on the fourth line and G is in the fourth space. On the keyboard they come just before ABC.

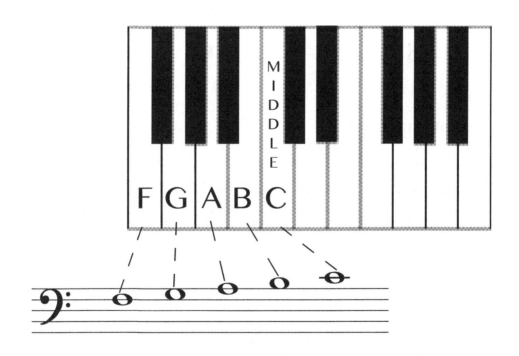

F G A B C

1. Write the following notes. Use whole notes.

F   G   A   B   C   F

2. Write the following notes. Use half notes.

G   C   F   A   B   C

3. Write the following notes. Use quarter notes.

C   B   A   G   F   B

4. Name the following notes

Music Match

Draw lines to match the notes with the correct answers.

F, half

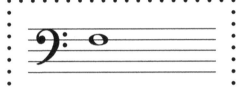

F, whole

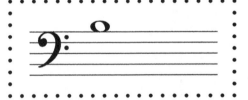

C, quarter

A, quarter

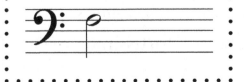

G, half

B, whole

Musical Terms - Dynamics

Two musical terms based on the words *piano* and *forte* mean very soft and very loud.

Term	Abbreviation	Meaning
pianissimo	*pp*	very soft
fortissimo	*ff*	very loud

Music Find a Word

Find and circle the words from the list below.

```
H L N Q U A R T E R
A O O K L O S O F T
L U T R M W H O L E
F D E S H F I U P Y
F O R T I S S I M O
T T K E Y B O A R D
O U Z M A P I A N O
P I A N I S S I M O
F O R T E B A S S L
T R E B L E A L I F
```

quarter	whole	half	keyboard	piano	pianissimo
forte	note	stem	loud	soft	fortissimo
bass	treble				

7

2nds and 3rds

We use *intervals* to measure distance in music. Intervals are given number names. By counting the letter names from one note to the next we can determine the number of the interval.

If we count from C to D there are 2 letter names: C - D. This is the interval of a 2nd.

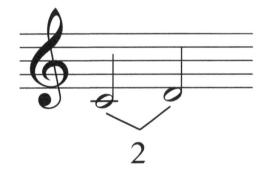

If we count from C to E there are 3 letter names: C - D - E. This is the interval of a 3rd.

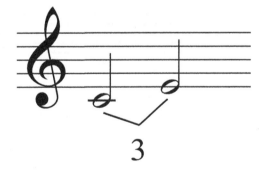

Intervals can be determined for notes that are descending too. The interval G to E is a 3rd. G - F - E

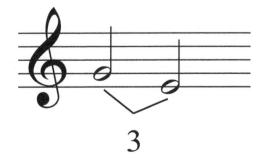

1. Name the following notes and write the interval number for each.

Name: <u>C</u>   <u>D</u>   ___   ___   ___   ___   ___

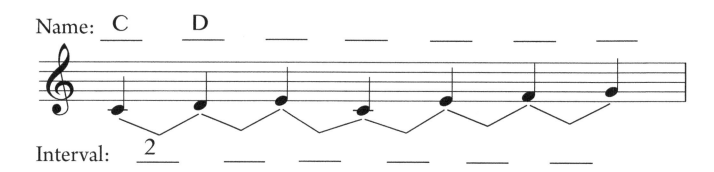

Interval: <u>2</u>   ___   ___   ___   ___   ___

Interval: ___   ___   ___   ___   ___   ___

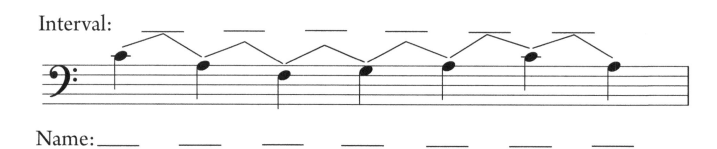

Name: ___   ___   ___   ___   ___   ___

2. Write these intervals above the given notes. Use whole notes.

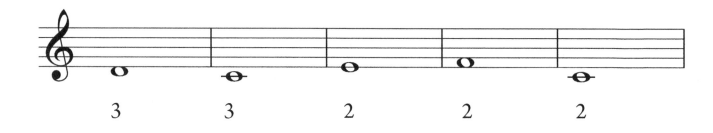

3   3   2   2   2

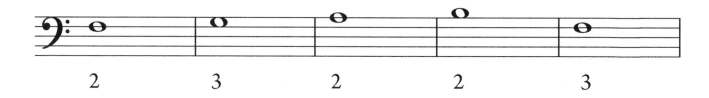

2   3   2   2   3

37

Musical Terms - Dynamics

Two musical terms using the words *piano* and *forte* mean moderately soft and moderately loud.

Term	Abbreviation	Meaning
mezzo piano	*mp*	moderately soft
mezzo forte	*mf*	moderately loud

Double Music Match

Draw lines to match the term with its abbreviation. Then match the abbreviation with its meaning.

mezzo piano	*p*	moderately soft
forte	*mf*	moderately loud
pianissimo	*mp*	soft
mezzo forte	*ff*	very soft
piano	*pp*	loud
fortissimo	*f*	very loud

History

The Orchestra

An *orchestra* is a large group of musicians who play together using different instruments.

The orchestra is divided into groups of instruments called *sections*. These sections include *strings, woodwinds, brass instruments* and *percussion instruments*.

The orchestra is led by the *conductor*.

The following picture shows where all the instruments are placed when the orchestra plays.

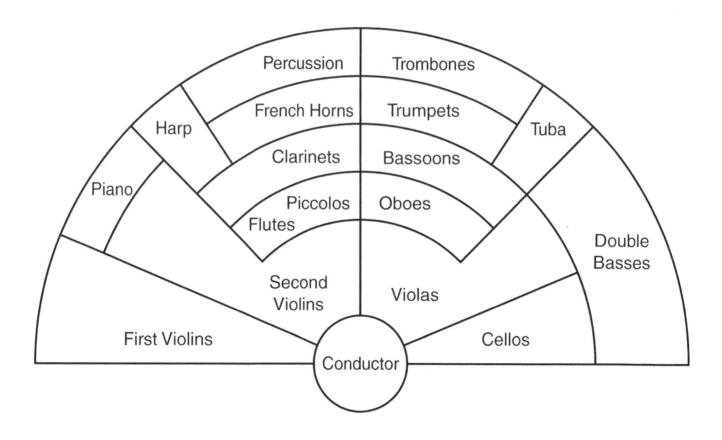

39

8

In order to organize music, beats or counts are grouped into sections called *measures*. Each measure has the same number of beats. *Bar lines* are used to divide the music into measures. A *double bar line* is used to indicate the end of the music.

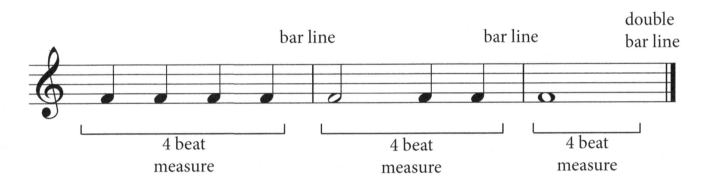

The Dotted Half Note

A half note with a dot beside it is called a *dotted half note*. It receives 3 counts or beats.

3 beats

The example below has 3 beats in each measure.

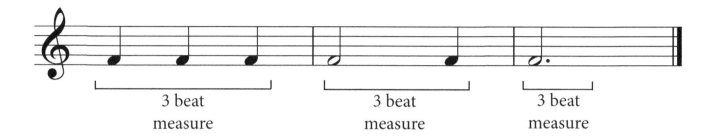

3 beat measure · 3 beat measure · 3 beat measure

1. Organize the beats by drawing a bar line every 4 beats.

2. Organize the beats by drawing a bar line every 3 beats.

3. Organize the beats by drawing a bar line every 2 beats.

Musical Terms - Dynamics

Sometimes composers ask us to get louder or softer when we play. There are terms and signs for this. Another word for decrescendo is ***diminuendo***.

Term	Sign	Meaning
crescendo		getting louder
decrescendo		getting softer

Draw signs for the following musical terms.

piano

fortissimo

crescendo

forte

mezzo piano

decrescendo

mezzo forte

diminuendo

pianissimo

MORE NOTES ON THE TREBLE STAFF

Space Notes

The notes in the spaces on the treble staff spell the word FACE.

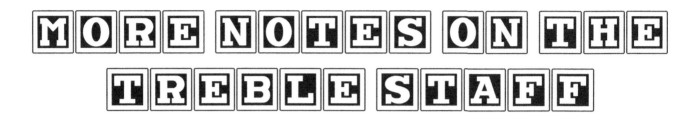

F A C E

1. Name of the following space notes.

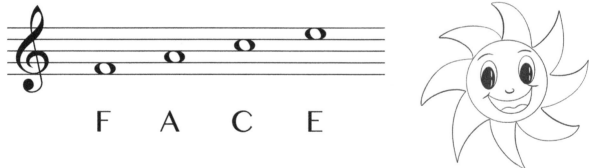

_____   _____   _____   _____   _____

2. Write the following notes in spaces.

A   E   C   F   A

Line Notes

The notes on the 5 lines of the treble staff are: EGBDF.

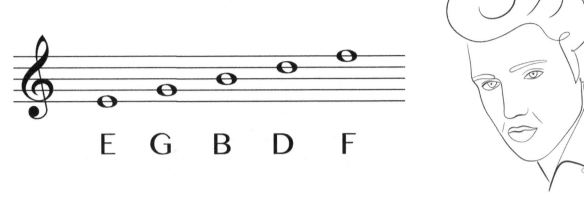

E   G   B   D   F

Sometimes it is helpful to make up a sentence to remember the note names. Here is one. See if you can make up your own.

Elvis' **G**uitar **B**roke **D**own **F**riday

3. Name of the following line notes.

_____   _____   _____   _____   _____

4. Write the following notes on lines.

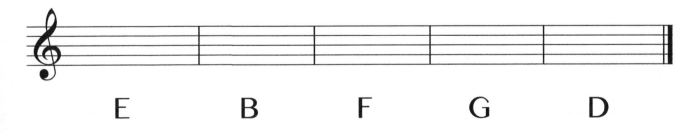

E   B   F   G   D

44   Lesson 9

5. Name the following notes.

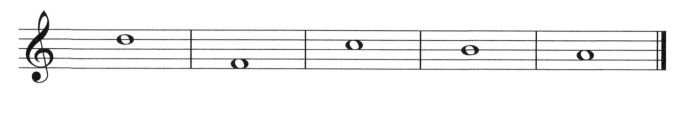

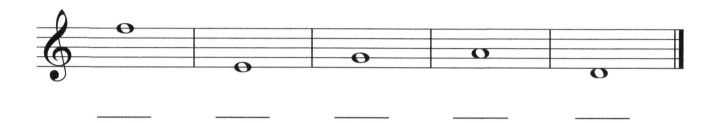

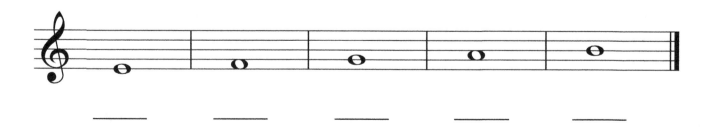

6. Write the following line notes.

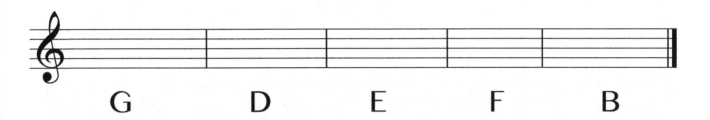

G   D   E   F   B

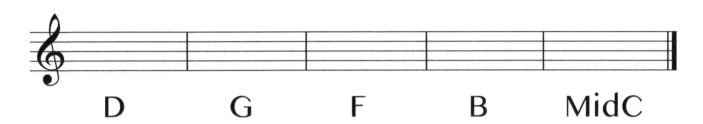

D   G   F   B   MidC

7. Write the following space notes.

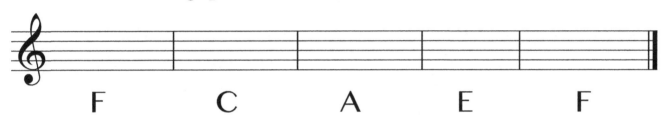

F   C   A   E   F

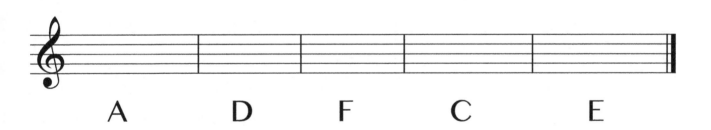

A   D   F   C   E

8. Write the following notes on lines or in spaces.

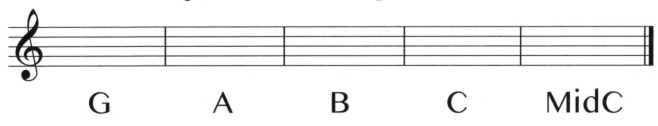

G   A   B   C   MidC

10

MORE NOTES ON THE BASS STAFF

Space Notes

The notes in the spaces on the BASS staff are: A C E G.

A   C   E   G

All   **C**ows   **E**at   **G**rass

1. Name of the following space notes.

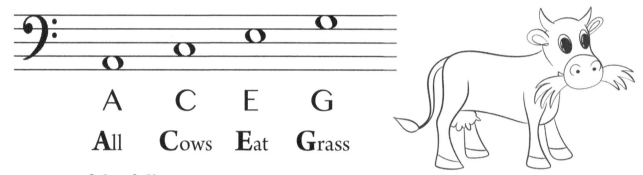

2. Write the following notes in spaces.

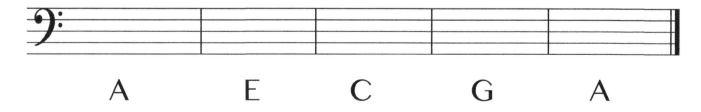

A   E   C   G   A

Line Notes

The notes on the 5 lines of the bass staff are: G B D F A.

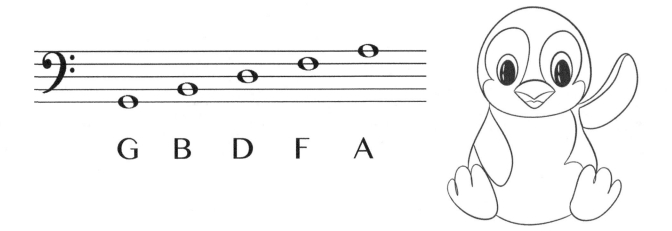

G   B   D   F   A

Good **B**irds **D**on't **F**ly **A**way

3. Name of the following line notes.

___   ___   ___   ___   ___

4. Write the following notes on lines.

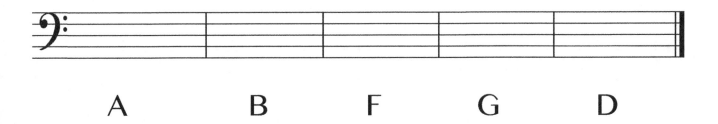

A   B   F   G   D

5. Name the following notes.

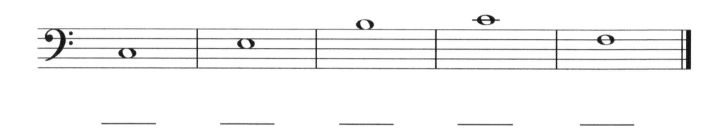

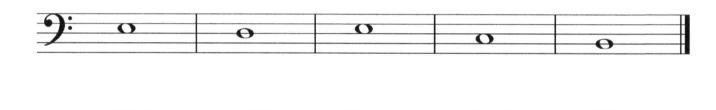

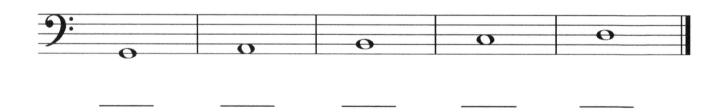

49

Lesson 9

6. Write the following line notes.

B   D   G   F   A

D   G   F   B   MidC

7. Write the following space notes.

A   C   G   E   A

C   E   G   C   A

8. Write the following notes on lines or in spaces.

G   A   B   C   MidC

Stem Direction Review

Many notes have stems. Stems may go up or stems may go down. There are specific rules for the direction of stems.

Stems Up

If a note is **below** the middle line its stem goes **up**.

Stems Down

If a note is **above** the middle line its stem goes **down**.

Stems Up or Down

If a note is **on** the middle line its stem may go **up** or **down**.

1. Add stems to the following notes.

2. Correct any stems that are going the wrong direction.

11

When you combine the treble and bass staffs together you get the *grand staff*. This staff is used by the piano because both clefs are needed to cover its large range. The treble clef is on the top and the bass clef is on the bottom. They are joined by a line and a brace or bracket. Middle C occurs in both clefs in the middle of the grand staff.

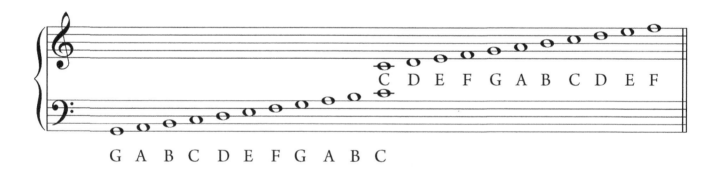

1. Copy the above grand staff in the space below.

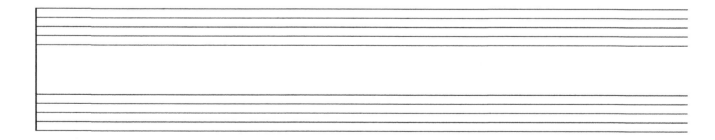

2. Name the following notes.

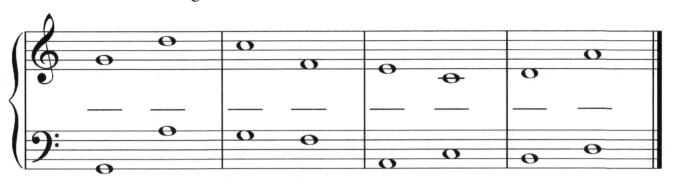

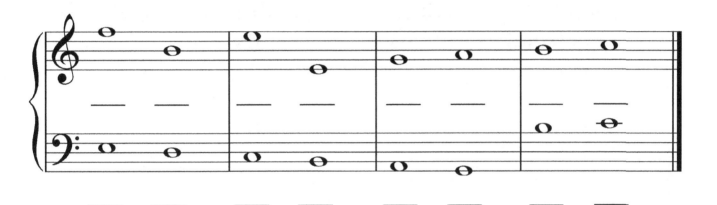

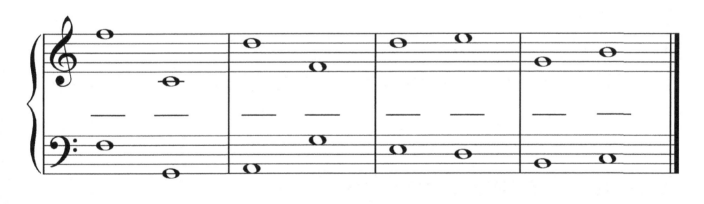

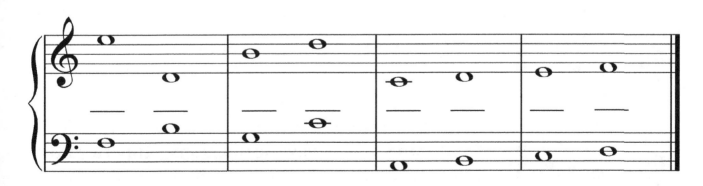

54

2. Write the following notes.

| Middle C in each clef | 3 different As | 3 different Bs | 3 different Cs |

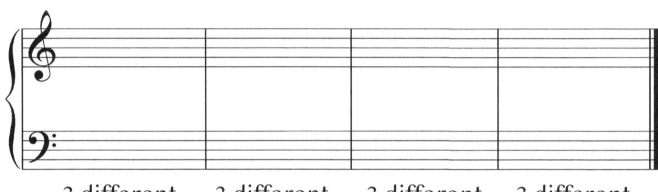

| 3 different Ds | 3 different Es | 3 different Fs | 3 different Gs |

Musical Terms and Signs

accent   a stressed note

slur   play the notes smoothly (legato)

History

String Instruments

The sound of the string instrument is created by vibrating strings. These strings are stretched across the hollow body of an instrument and are played by plucking or drawing a bow across them. Instruments in the string section include the violin, the viola, the cello and the double bass.

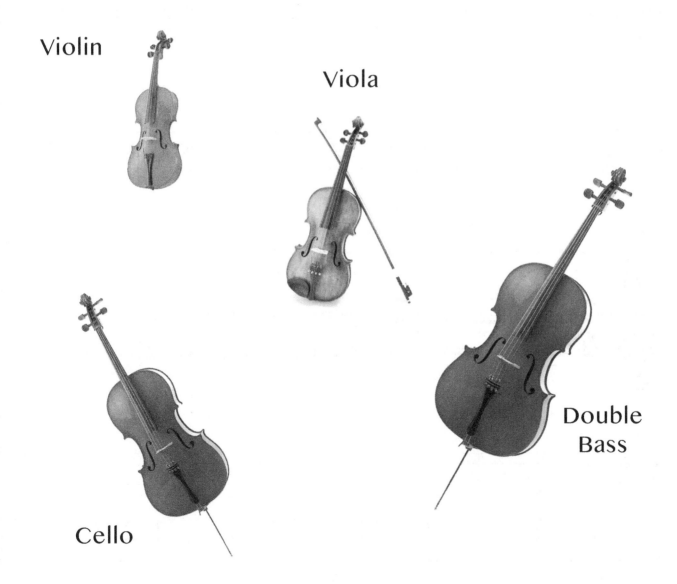

Violin

Viola

Cello

Double Bass

 Lesson 11

12

Two numbers are placed at the beginning of every piece of music. These two numbers are called the *time signature*. The time signature tells us how many beats or counts are in each measure and which note is worth one beat.

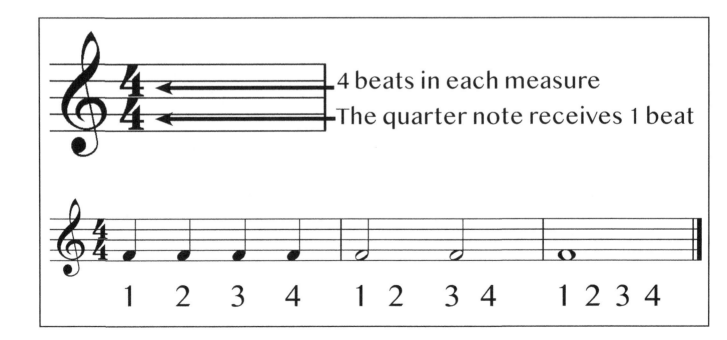

4 beats in each measure

The quarter note receives 1 beat

1 2 3 4   1 2 3 4   1 2 3 4

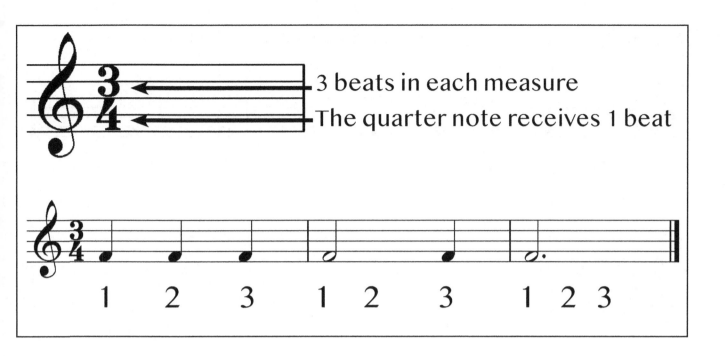

3 beats in each measure

The quarter note receives 1 beat

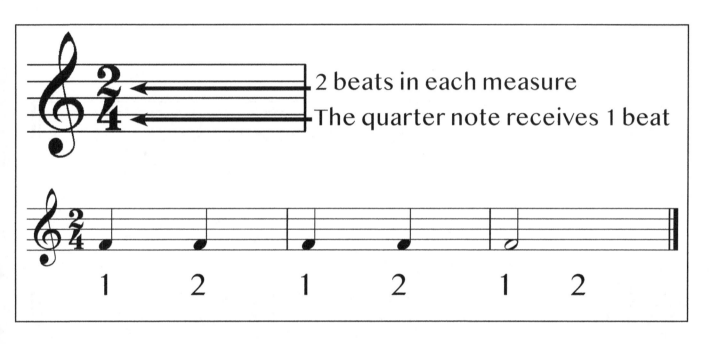

2 beats in each measure

The quarter note receives 1 beat

Lesson 12

1. Write the beats below the notes as shown in the first measure.

1   2   3   4

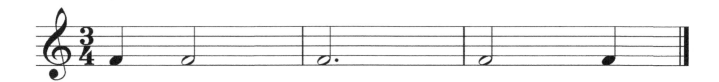

2. Add time signatures at the beginning of each line.

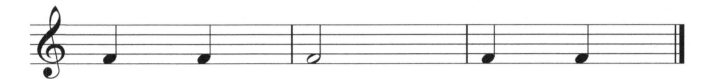

3. Add bar lines according to the time signatures.

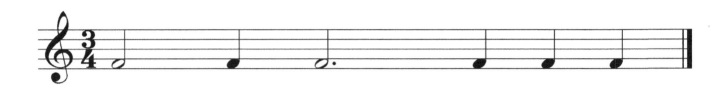

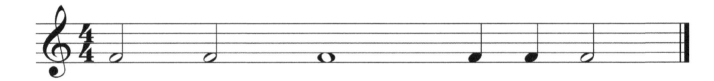

61

4. Add one note in each box to complete each measure

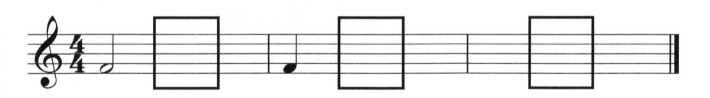

13

Silence in music is as important as sound. Silence in music is indicated by signs called *rests*. Rests use the same names as notes. A four count note is a whole note. A four count rest is a *whole rest*. A one count note is a quarter note. A one count rest is a *quarter rest*.

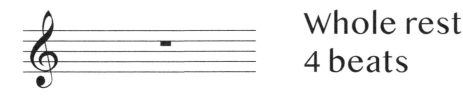

Whole rest
4 beats

Half rest
2 beats

Quarter rest
1 beat

     Lesson 13

1. Write the following rests.

Quarter rest = _____ beat.

Half rest = _____ beats.

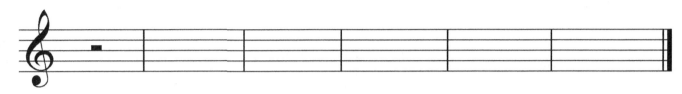

Whole rest = _____ beats

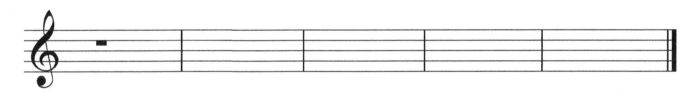

2. Add one rest in each box to complete each measure.

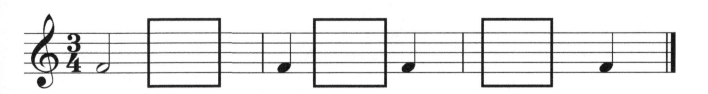

Draw lines connecting the rhythms and the time signatures

History

Woodwind Instruments

Woodwind instruments are a group of wind instruments made of a long hollow tube of wood or metal. The sound is made by blowing air through a very thin piece of shaved wood called a reed, or across a small mouthpiece. Finger holes along the instrument are opened and closed to change the notes. The oboe, clarinet, bassoon, and flute are examples of woodwind instruments.

The Clarinet

The *clarinet* is a long, black woodwind instrument. It has a mouthpiece with one reed and keys down the sides. You play a clarinet by blowing in the mouthpiece and making the reed vibrate. The sound changes by pressing the keys.

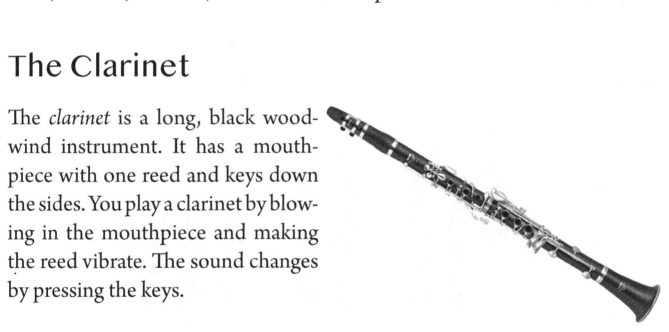

The Oboe

The *oboe* is a woodwind instrument with a double reed at the tip. Sound is made when a person blows through the mouthpiece. Sounds are changed by pushing down keys.

14

Half Steps

A *half step* is the distance from one key to the very next key on the keyboard. It is the shortest distance between the keys on the keyboard.

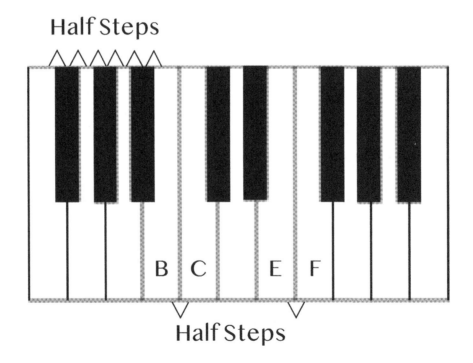

Most half steps occur between black and white keys. There are 2 half steps between white keys on the keyboard. These are between B and C and E and F. The very next key above B is C. This is a half step. The very next key above E is F. This is also a half step.

Whole Steps

2 half steps make a whole step. On the keyboard there is always one key be-tweeen the two keys of a whole step.

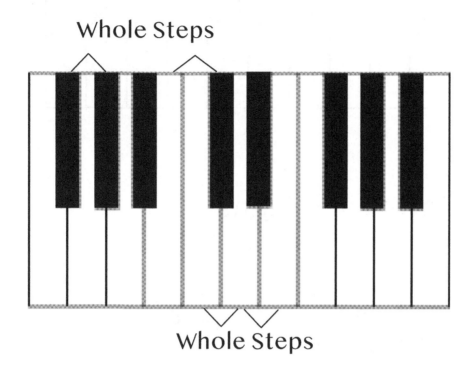

1. On the following keyboard, color the keys that are an half step above the keys marked X.

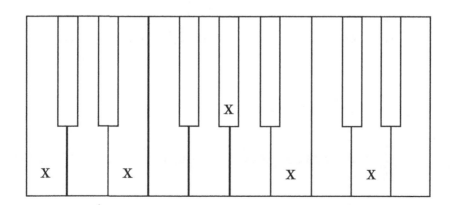

2. On the following keyboard, color the keys that are a whole step above the keys marked X.

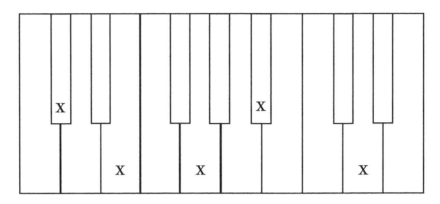

Musical Terms and Signs

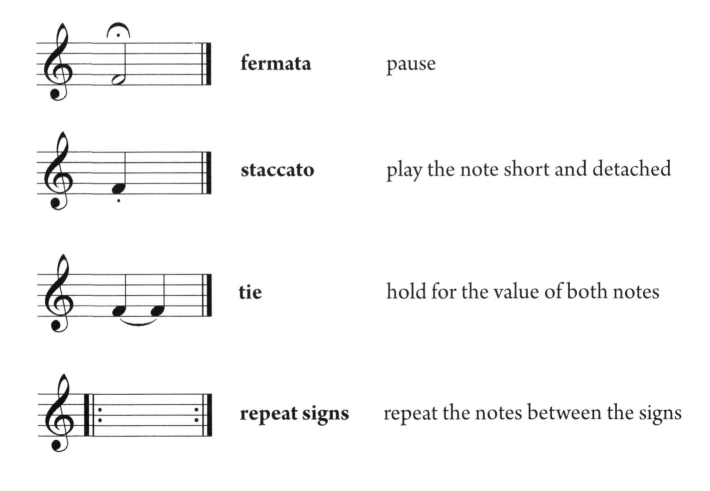

fermata　　　　pause

staccato　　　　play the note short and detached

tie　　　　hold for the value of both notes

repeat signs　　　repeat the notes between the signs

15

This is a sharp.
A sharp raises a note by one half step.

A sharp note is a black note that is just to the right (or above) most white keys. Sharps get their names from the white key below or to the left. On the musical score, sharps are written in front of the note. When we say the name of the sharp, we say "F sharp," "C sharp," etc.

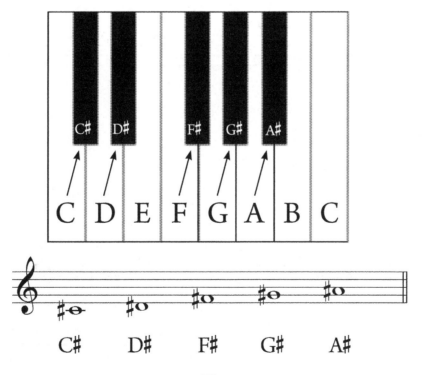

The opening in the middle of the sharp is placed in the same space or on the same line as the note it is raising.

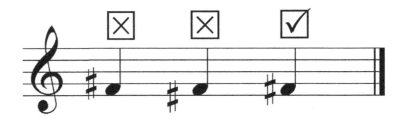

1. Write a sharp in front of each note and give its letter name.

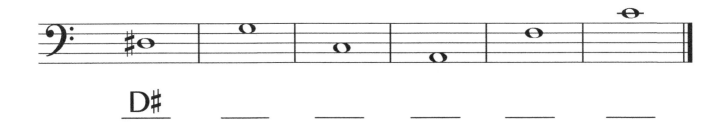

D♯ ___ ___ ___ ___ ___

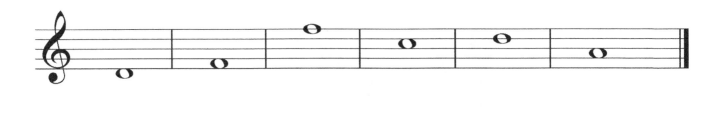

___ ___ ___ ___ ___ ___

___ ___ ___ ___ ___ ___

2. Name the following notes. Draw lines to the correct key on the keyboard.

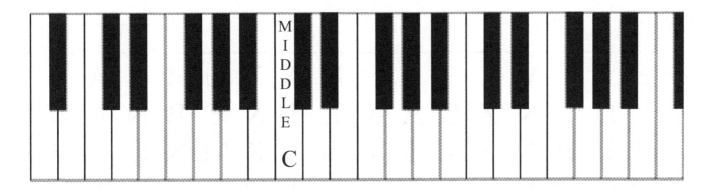

____ ____ ____ ____ ____ ____

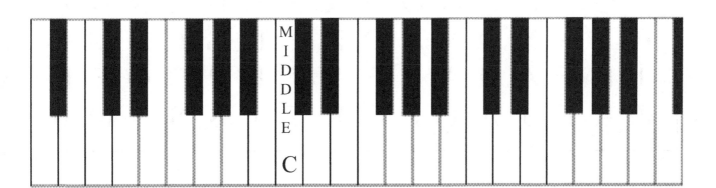

____ ____ ____ ____ ____ ____

Music Word Search

```
F T I M E S I G N A T U R E A S
E D L K Z B A R L I N E B N F W
R E P E A T S I G N R M N D J H
M C G E R T T I E I U E Q I W O
A V R Q Z X A D F G Q A J M U L
T C A Y C V C Z X L U S F I Y E
A V N O T E C R A T A U O N W S
M N D P S H A R P E R R R U S T
G T S L J E T B Z X T E T E F E
E G T H A D O H R R E H E N N P
P I A N O X A O Z E R G E D M L
J E F A H A L F S T E P D O E K
Z A F J A L F O R T I S S I M O
```

Bar line	Fermata	Diminuendo
Measure	Sharp	Repeat sign
Tie	Quarter	Whole step
Rest	Piano	Half step
Note	Fortissimo	Time signature
Staccato	Forte	Grand staff

16

This is a flat.
A flat lowers a note by one half step.

A flat note is a black note that is just to the left (or below) most white keys. Flats get their names from the white key above or to the right. On the musical score, flats are written in front of the note. When we say the name of the flat, we say "D flat," "E flat," etc.

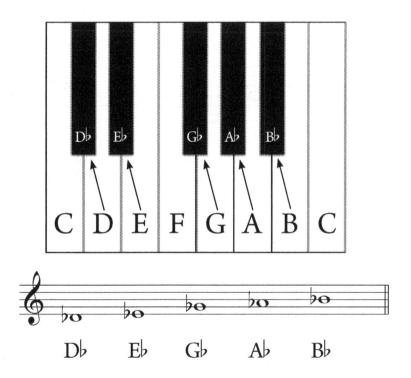

Lesson 16

Be sure to place the flat sign correctly in front of each note.

1. Write a flat in front of each note and give its letter name.

<u>G♭</u> ___ ___ ___ ___ ___

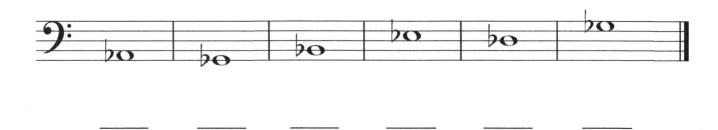

___ ___ ___ ___ ___ ___

___ ___ ___ ___ ___ ___

2. Name the following notes. Draw lines to the correct key on the keyboard.

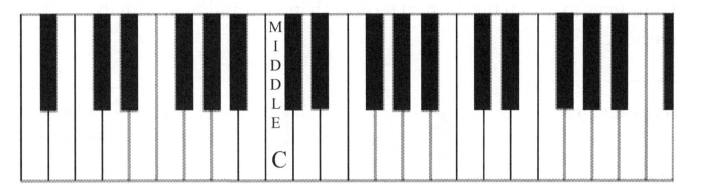

___ ___ ___ ___ ___ ___

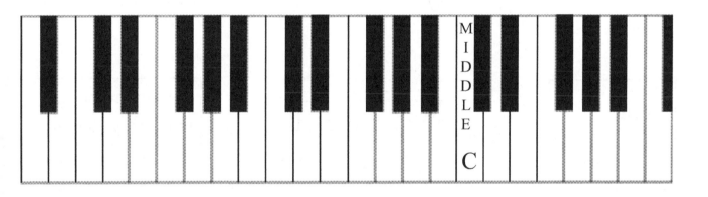

___ ___ ___ ___ ___ ___

Double Music Match

Draw lines to match the musical term with its sign and then with its meaning.

repeat signs	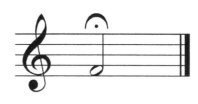	repeat the notes between the signs
tie		hold for the value of both notes
fermata		pause
slur		play the notes smoothly (legato)
staccato	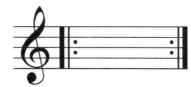	play the note short and detached
accent		a stressed note

17

This is a natural.
A natural cancels a flat or sharp.

Any note that isn't sharp or flat is already a natural. If there are no sharp or flat notes the natural is not used. Naturals are placed on the same line or in the space as the note they are altering.

A natural can raise or lower the pitch of a note. When a natural cancels a sharp it lowers the pitch one half step.

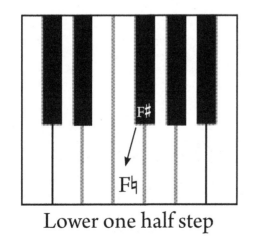

Lower one half step

F# F♮

When a natural cancels a flat it raises the pitch one half step.

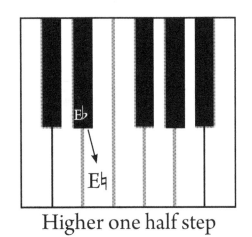

Higher one half step

1. Write natural signs before each note. Name the note.

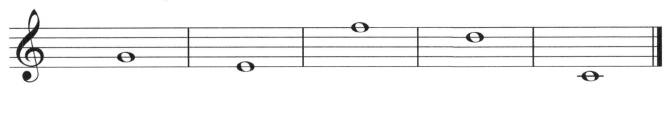

_____   _____   _____   _____   _____

_____   _____   _____   _____   _____

_____   _____   _____   _____   _____

2. Name the following notes. Color them on the keyboard.

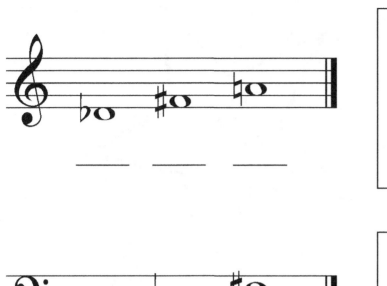
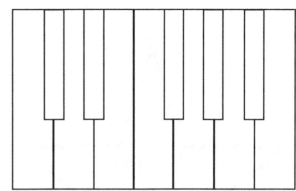

_____ _____ _____

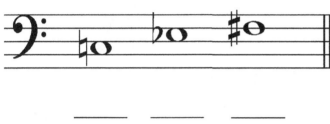
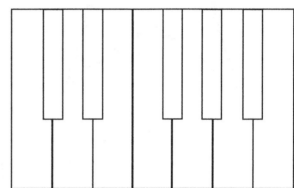

_____ _____ _____

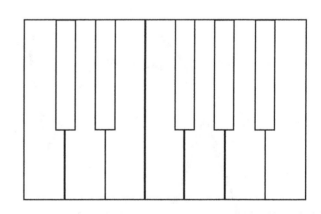

_____ _____ _____

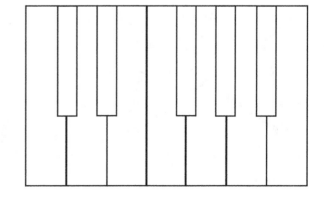

_____ _____ _____

80   Lesson 17

Half Step Review

What is a half step above G?
_____

What is a half step below F♯?
_____

What is a half step below A?
_____

What is a half step above B♭?
_____

What is a half step below C?
_____

Circle all the half steps.

History

Brass Instruments

Brass instruments are really made of brass. They are long tubes of curled up metal with flared ends called bells. You play a brass instrument by buzzing your lips into a mouthpiece. This makes air vibrate through the tubes and creates sound. The main instruments of the brass family include the trumpet, horn, trombone, and tuba.

The Trumpet

The *trumpet* is the highest sounding and oldest member of the brass family. The player presses three valves with the fingers of the right hand to obtain different pitches. There are 2 to 4 trumpets in the orchestra.

The French Horn

The *French horn* or *horn* consists of about 12 feet of brass tubing wound into a circle. The player obtains different notes on the horn by pressing valves with the left hand. There are usually 4 horns in an orchestra but there may be as many as 8.

18

An eighth note receives one half of a beat. When an eighth note occurs by itself it has a flag attached to the stem. The flag always goes on the right side of the stem.

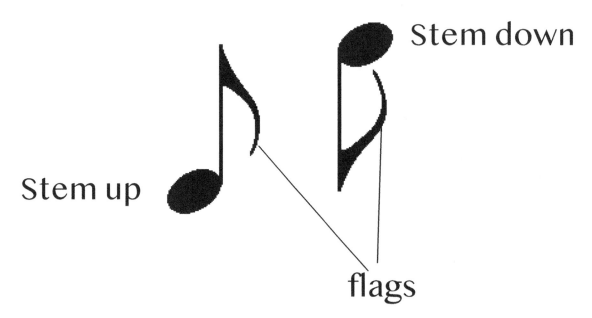

Stem down

Stem up

flags

1. Change the following notes into eighth notes by filling them in and adding stems and flags. Follow the rules of stem direction.

One eighth note equals one half of a beat.

$$\eighthnote = \text{½ beat}$$

Two eighth notes may be joined with a line called a *beam*. Two eighth notes are equal to one beat.

$$\eighthnote + \eighthnote = \text{beamed eighths} = 1 \text{ beat}$$

2. Practice drawing pairs of eighth notes in each measure.

This is an *eighth rest*. It is equal to one half beat of silence.

$$\text{𝄾} = \text{½ beat silence}$$

3. On the staff, the eighth rest is placed the middle of the staff in space two and three. Practice drawing eighth rests in each measure.

Counting Eighths

Because there are 2 eighths in every beat, the count is a little different. To divide the beat into 2 equal parts it helps to say "and" for the second eighth note in each beat. In 2/4 time there are 2 beats in each measure. We can divide each beat into 2 parts by saying the word "and" after the number.

This works for other time signatures. For example, in 3/4 time we count 1 "and" 2 "and" 3 "and." Since we are dividing each beat into 2 parts, and the quarter note is worth a whole beat, it gets both the number and the "and."

1. Write the counts below each note and rest. Use "+" for the word and.

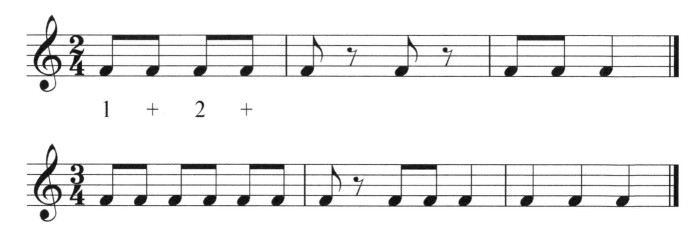

2. Put ♪ or ♩ into the box to complete each measure.

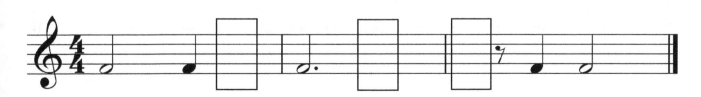

3. Add the correct time signature at the beginning of each measure.

19

Most notes are written on the staff. However, there are many more notes available to us. When a note goes above or below the staff we use small lines called *ledger lines* to extend the range of the staff. These notes show where the staff would be if it had more than 5 lines and 4 spaces. Ledger lines never occur without a note attached.

These are a few of the ledger line notes above and below the treble and bass staves. When writing ledger line notes, make the ledger lines the same distance apart as the lines of the staff.

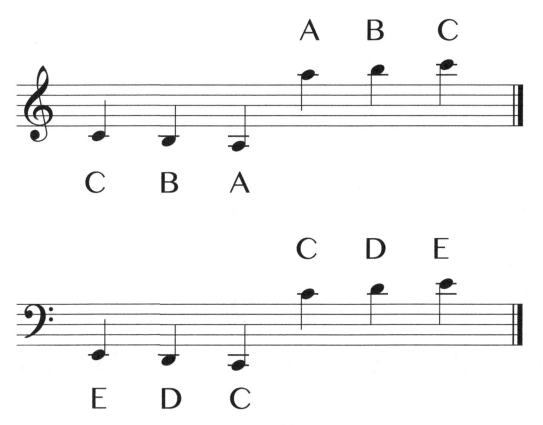

1. Name the following notes.

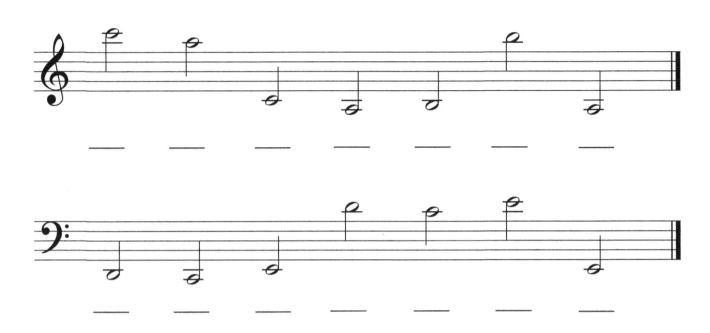

2. Write the following ledger line notes above each staff.

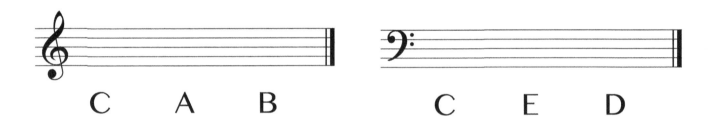

C   A   B   C   E   D

3. Write the following ledger line notes below each staff.

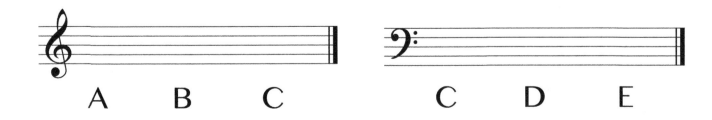

A   B   C   C   D   E

4. Name the following notes.

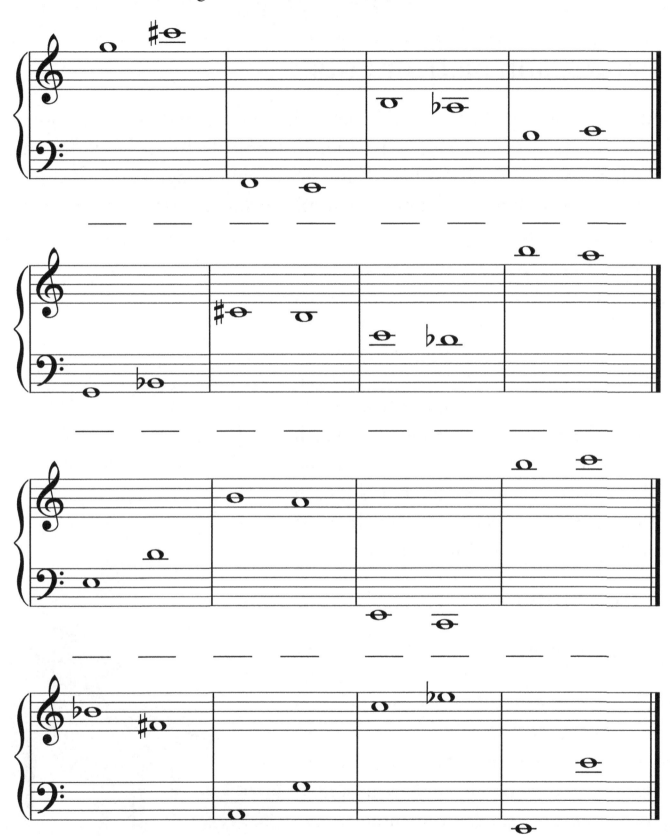

History

Percussion Instruments

All instruments that are played by being hit with something are *percussion* instruments. There are many percussion instruments. Examples of these are the timpani or kettle drum, bass drum, snare drum, gong, triangle, tambourine, cymbols, chimes, xylophone, marimba, piano, celesta, castanets, maracas, and many more.

The Timpani

Timpani, also called kettle drums, were the first drums to be used in the orchestra over 300 years ago. It is the only drum that can be tuned to produce definite pitches. It has a large kettle-shaped bottom, over which the skin of the drumhead is stretched. The player uses a pedal to tighten and loosen the drumhead to change the pitch. Most orchestras use three or four timpani.

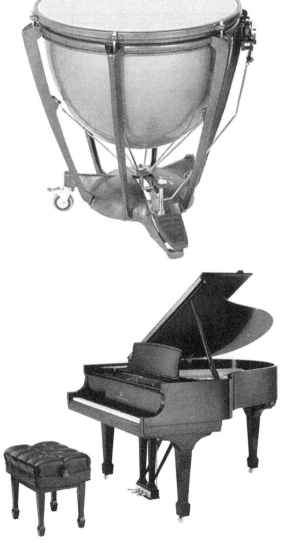

The Piano

The *piano* is a stringed keyboard instrument. Its strings are struck by hammers which are connected to the keys. It could be classified as a string or a percussion instrument. There are 88 keys on a modern piano, and each one is a different note. It was originally called the pianoforte, because it could play both soft (piano) and loud (forte).

20

The C Major Scale

A *scale* has 8 notes that move by step. When a scale goes up it is *ascending*. When a scale goes down it is *descending*.

Here is the *C major scale* going up, or ascending.

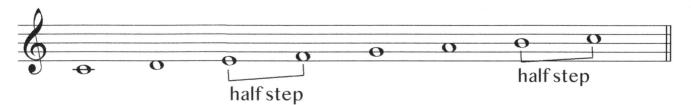

half step

half step

The half steps are marked with a bracket. In a major scale there is a half step between notes 3 and 4 and notes 7 and 8. Whole steps occur between the other notes. This scale uses the white keys from C to C on the keyboard.

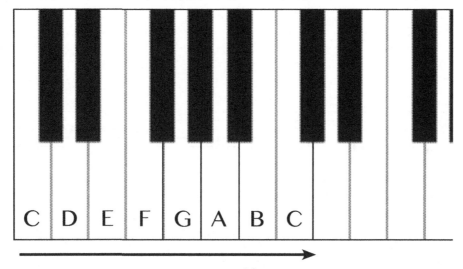

Here is the C major scale going down, or descending.

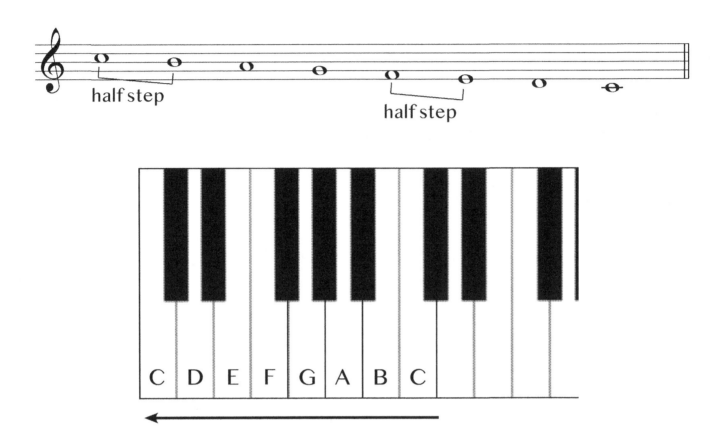

half step

half step

C D E F G A B C

The first note of any scale is called the *tonic*. The tonic of C major is C. This is the most important note in the scale. The tonic is marked with a **T** in the C major scale below. The tonic occurs at the beginning and at the end.

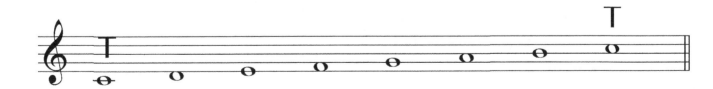

T

T

1. Mark the tonic notes (T) on the following C major scales. Draw a bracket under the half steps.

2. Mark with an "X" the notes of the C major scale on the keyboard.

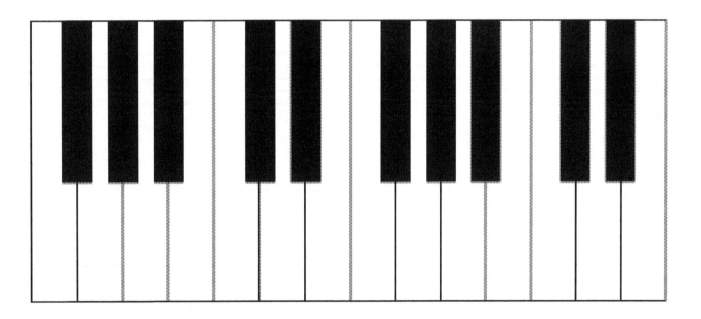

3. Write the following C major scales. Mark the tonic (T).

In half notes, ascending

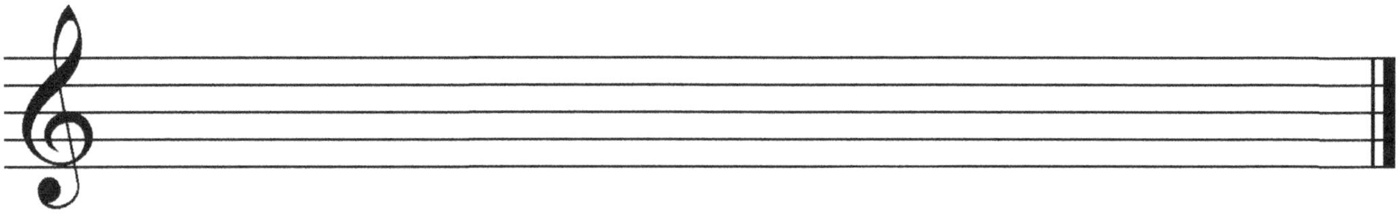

In whole notes, descending

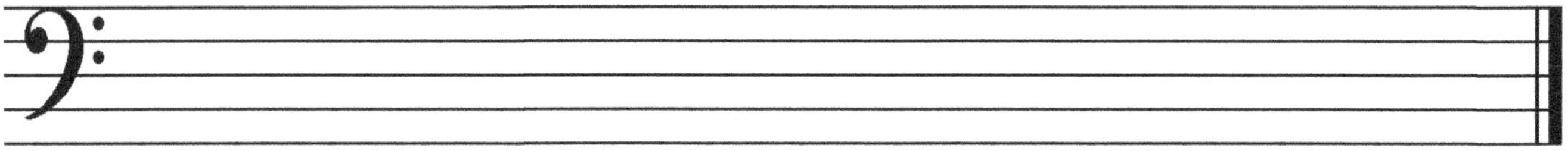

In quarter notes, descending

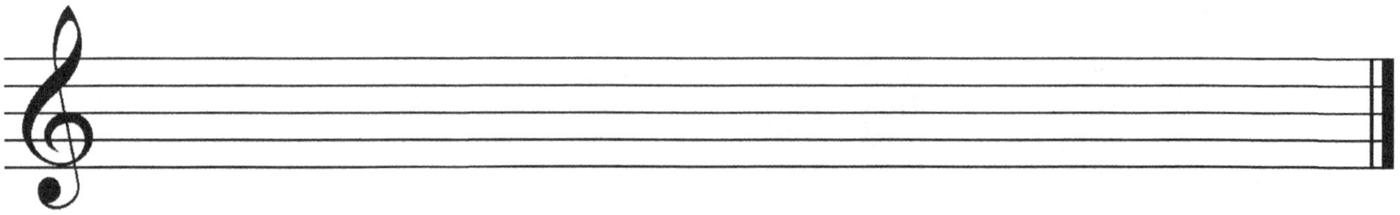

In dotted half notes, ascending

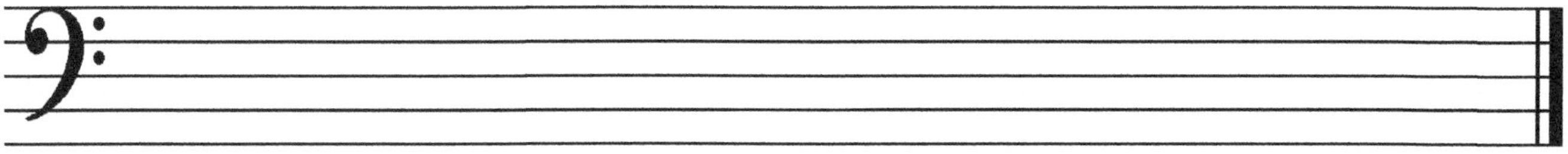

21

The A Natural Minor Scale

Another type of scale is the *minor scale*. Minor scales, like major scales, have 8 notes that move by step.

Here is the *A natural minor scale* ascending.

The tonic of the A natural minor scale is the first note, A. There are half steps between notes 2 and 3 and notes 5 and 6.

On the keyboard this scale is played on the white keys from A to A.

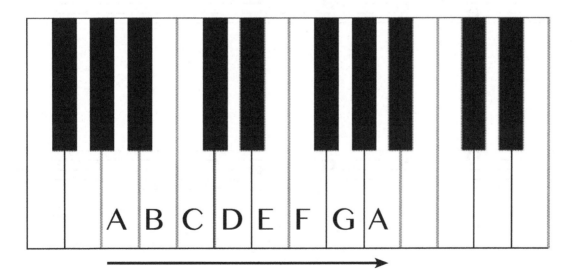

Here is the A natural minor scale ascending.

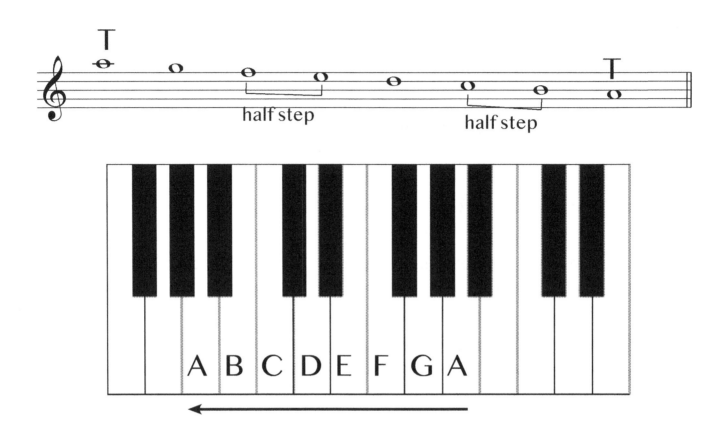

1. Mark the tonic notes (T) on the following A natural minor scales. Draw a bracket under the half steps.

2. Write the following A natural minor scales. Mark the tonic (T).

In dotted half notes, ascending

In whole notes, descending

In quarter notes, descending

In half notes, ascending

Musical Instrument Quiz

Check the section of the orchestra where each instrument is found.

Clarinet

❑Woodwinds ❑Brass ❑Strings ❑Percussion

Violin

❑Woodwinds ❑Brass ❑Strings ❑Percussion

Timpani

❑Woodwinds ❑Brass ❑Strings ❑Percussion

Cello

❑Woodwinds ❑Brass ❑Strings ❑Percussion

Oboe

❑Woodwinds ❑Brass ❑Strings ❑Percussion

Xylophone

❑Woodwinds ❑Brass ❑Strings ❑Percussion

French Horn

❑Woodwinds ❑Brass ❑Strings ❑Percussion

Piano

❑Woodwinds ❑Brass ❑Strings ❑Percussion

Trumpet

❑Woodwinds ❑Brass ❑Strings ❑Percussion

22

MORE INTERVALS

An interval can be defined as the distance from one note to the next. Intervals are given number names. For now, we will study the intervals from 1 to 8. There are two basic types of intervals, harmonic and melodic.

A *harmonic interval* is when two notes are played or sung at the same time. A *melodic interval* is when two notes are played or sung one after the other.

Harmonic   Melodic

The interval number is determined by counting up from the lowest note to the highest note.

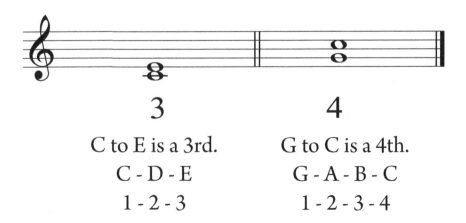

3	4
C to E is a 3rd.	G to C is a 4th.
C - D - E	G - A - B - C
1 - 2 - 3	1 - 2 - 3 - 4

       Lesson 22

The interval number is determined by counting up from the lowest note to the highest note. This is done even if the lowest note comes after the highest note.

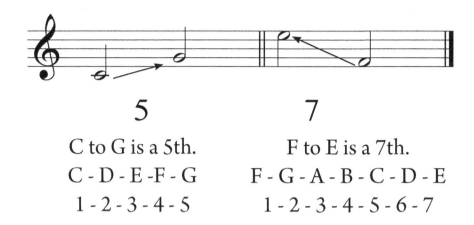

5	7
C to G is a 5th.	F to E is a 7th.
C - D - E -F - G	F - G - A - B - C - D - E
1 - 2 - 3 - 4 - 5	1 - 2 - 3 - 4 - 5 - 6 - 7

These are the intervals from 1 to 8 using D as the lowest note for each.

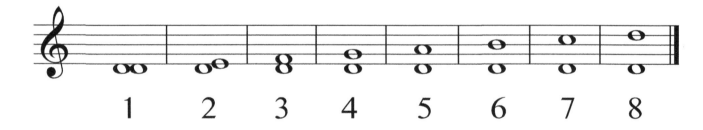

1   2   3   4   5   6   7   8

1. Write the number name of the following harmonic intervals.

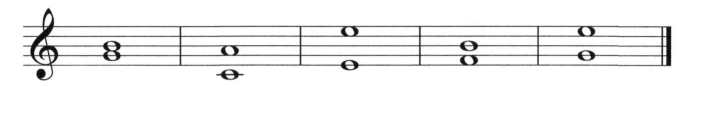

—   —   —   —   —

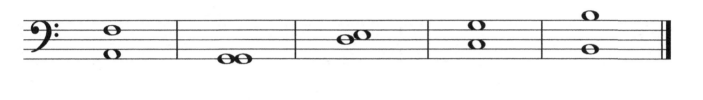

—   —   —   —   —

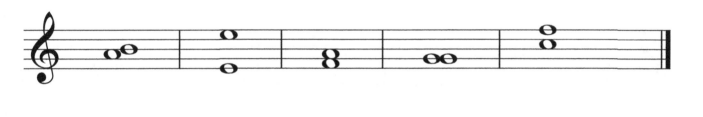

—   —   —   —   —

—   —   —   —   —

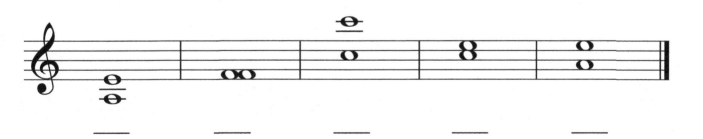

—   —   —   —   —

2. Write the number name of the following melodic intervals.

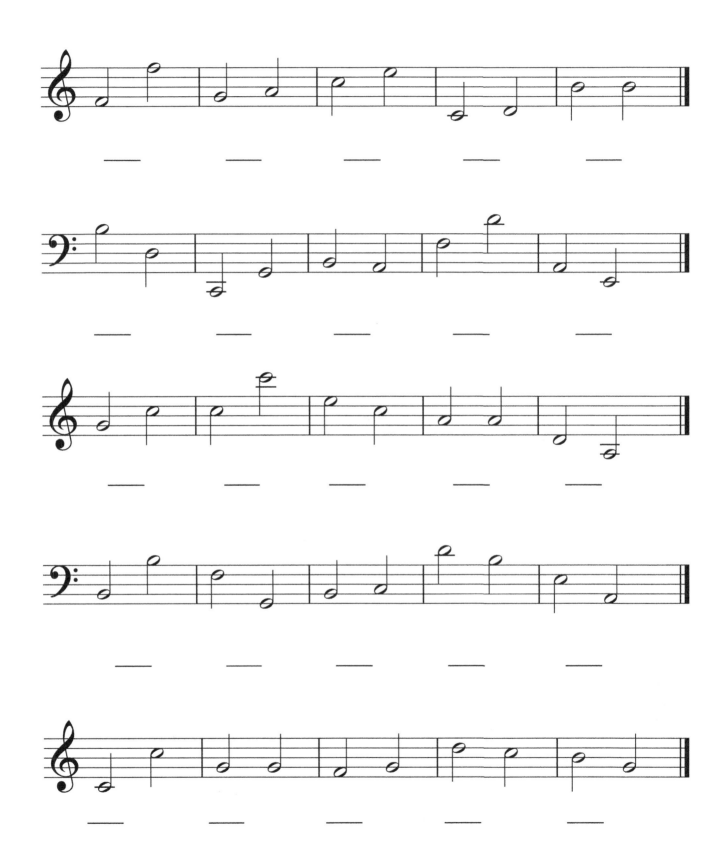

You may be asked to write an interval above a given note. These are the steps for writing an interval above a given note.

Write a 6th above the following note.

1. Name the given note. Here, it is D.

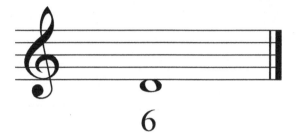

2. Count up 6 notes starting at D.

D-E-F-G-A-B
1-2-3-4-5-6

3. Write the note that is 6 notes above D.
   The answer is B.

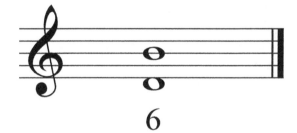

1. Write harmonic intervals above the given notes.

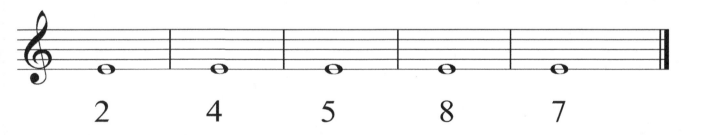

2   4   5   8   7

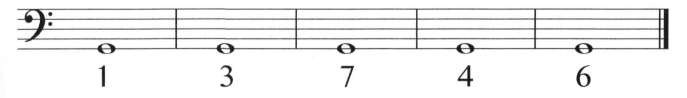

1   3   7   4   6

2. Add stems to the following notes. Identify the interval numbers in the boxes below the staff.

23

The Tonic Triad

A *chord* is a group of notes that are played at the same time.

A *triad* is a three note chord. "**Tri**" means three. A **tri**cycle has a 3 wheels.
A **tri**angle has 3 sides. A **tri**ad has 3 notes.

A *tonic triad* is made up of notes 1, 3, and 5 of a major or minor scale.
It is called the tonic triad because it is built on the tonic or first note of a scale.
Notes 1, 3, and 5 of the C major scale are C - E - G.

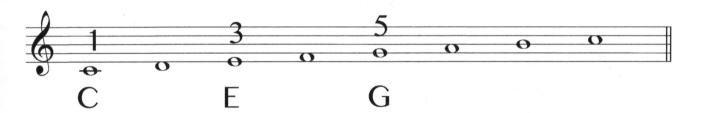

The *C major triad* is shown below.

Under the triad is an "I". I is the Roman numeral for the number 1. This Roman numeral is called the *chord symbol*. This is a capitol 'I'. Major triads get a capitol Roman numeral.

The tonic triad of C can also be called the I chord, because it is built on scale degree 1 of the C major scale.

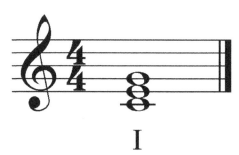

When all three notes of the triad are played together the triad is *solid or blocked*.
When the three notes are played one after the other the triad is *broken*.

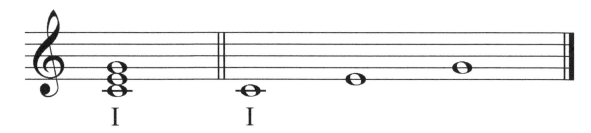

1. Write the C major scale ascending in the treble clef. Label notes 1, 3, and 5 of the scale. Write the C major triad in solid form in the second bar. Add the Roman numeral chord symbol.

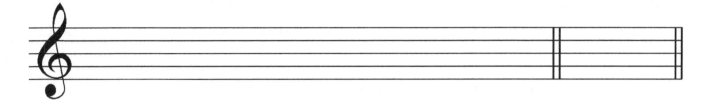

2. Write the C major scale ascending in the bass clef. Label notes 1, 3, and 5 of the scale. Write the C major triad in solid form in the second bar. Add the Roman numeral chord symbol.

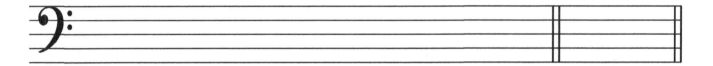

The A Minor Triad

If we build a triad on notes 1, 3, and 5 of the A natural minor scale, we get the *tonic triad in A minor*. This is also known as the *A minor triad*.

The A minor triad is a *minor* triad. The C major triad is a *major* triad.

If you play the A minor triad and compare it with the C major triad, you will notice it has a different quality of sound. This is because minor and major triads **are** different. Some say the minor triad sounds darker or sadder. This is a matter of opinion, but the two triads certainly have a different character.

The lowercase Roman numeral for 1 is "i". Minor triads use lowercase Roman numerals in the chord symbols. The tonic triad in A minor is built on 1 of the A minor scale, and it gets a lowercase "**i**" for a chord symbol.

Solid/Blocked   Broken

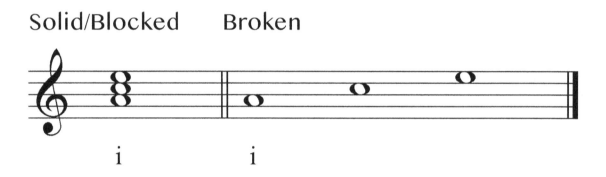

1. Write the A natural minor scale ascending in the treble clef. Label notes 1, 3, and 5 of the scale. Write the A minor triad in solid form in the second bar. Add the Roman numeral chord symbol.

2. Write the A natural minor scale ascending in the bass clef. Label notes 1, 3, and 5 of the scale. Write the A minor triad in solid form in the second bar. Add the Roman numeral chord symbol.

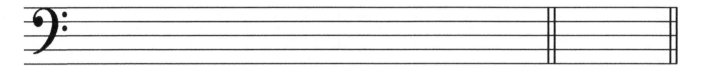

3. Build solid triads on the following notes. Label each chord with a Roman numeral chord symbol.

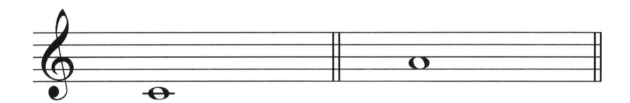

4. Name the following triads as C major or A minor.

_____   _____   _____   _____

5. Write the following broken triads. Label each with a chord symbol.

C major   A minor

A minor   C major

6. Name the following triads and then color the notes on the keyboard.

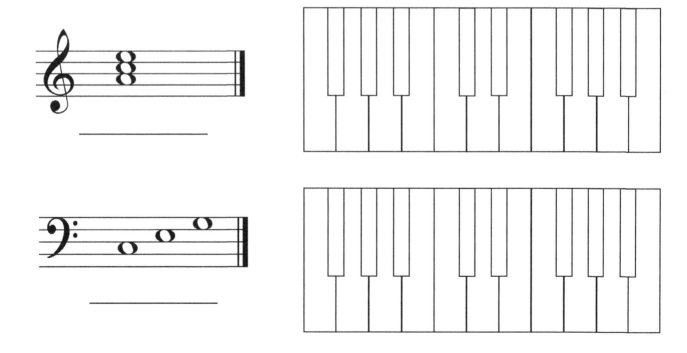

_____

_____

TERMS AND SIGNS

Dynamics

Dynamics refer to how loud or soft we play.

piano	*p*	soft
forte	*f*	loud
mezzo piano	*mp*	moderately soft
mezzo forte	*mf*	moderately loud
pianissimo	*pp*	very soft
fortissimo	*ff*	very loud
crescendo	<	getting louder
decrescendo	>	getting softer

Signs

	accent	a stressed note
	slur	play the notes smoothly (legato)
	fermata	pause
	staccato	play the note short and detached
	tie	hold for the value of both notes
	repeat signs	repeat the notes between the signs

113

Made in the USA
Middletown, DE
20 September 2023